Tips for Talking and Reading Together

Stories are a fun and reassuring way of introducing children to new experiences.

- Talk about the title and the pictures on the cover.
- Talk about your child's expectations and emotions.
- Read the story with your child.
- Have fun finding the hidden combs.

When you've read the story:

- Discuss the Talk About ideas on page 27.
- Look at the pictures and vocabulary on pages 28–29.
- Have fun finding the objects in the pictures.
- Do the fun activity at the end.

Have fun!

Find the combs hidden in every picture.

At the Hairdresser

Roderick Hunt • Annemarie Young
Alex Brychta

OXFORD
UNIVERSITY PRESS

Mum had some old photos.

"This is me with my family," she said, "when I was a little girl."

4

Biff looked at the photos. She had
an idea. "Let's have a family photo,
and give one to Gran as a surprise!"

"That's a good idea," said Dad.
"Gran would love it. But we need to
look smart."

"We should all go to the
hairdresser," said Mum. "Kipper's
hair needs cutting and so does
Chip's. We'll all have a trim."

The next day, they all went into
town. Chip and Dad stopped at the
barber shop.

"We'll see you later," said Dad.

"Come on, Biff and Kipper,"
said Mum, "we're going to the
hairdresser."

The hairdresser was called Jon.

"Have you brought your teddy in for a fur cut?" said Jon.

Kipper laughed. He liked Jon.

Jon had a special seat. He put it
over the arms of the chair.

"This is the driving seat," he said.
"Climb up and let's go."

"Here's the spray to make your hair wet," said Jon. "You can try it on Ted."

"And here's the magic gown," said
Jon. "This keeps Teddy safe while I
cut your hair."

"Keep Ted still," said Jon. "Don't
let him escape."

Jon sprayed Kipper's hair and
began to cut it.

"Now keep *very* still," said Jon.
"I'm going to cut around your ears."
"It tickles!" said Kipper. He found
it hard to keep still, but he did.

"You were very good, Kipper,"
said Jon.

Kipper was pleased. He looked at
Biff. She was having her hair cut too.

The hairdresser was cutting Biff's fringe. Biff had her eyes shut.

"Put your tongue in," said Kipper, "or you'll get hairs on it."

Mum was pleased with Biff and
Kipper. "You have been good," she
said. "We all look much better!"

Dad and Chip came home.

"Oh no!" said Mum.

"We've had new haircuts!"
said Dad. "Don't you like them?"

Dad and Chip had wigs on. They were playing a trick.

"You are funny, Dad," said Biff.

"I have an idea!" said Mum.

The next day, the family went to have the photo taken for Gran.

"You all look very smart," said the photographer.

The photographer made
them sit close together.
"Look at the camera,"
she said. "Smile!"

"Now we want you to take another
photo," said Mum.

"My goodness!" said the
photographer.

All the family had funny wigs on.
"This will make Gran laugh,"
said Chip.

"Which picture shall we give Gran first?" asked Biff. "This one or the proper one?"

"This one, of course," said Mum.

"My goodness!" said Gran, when
she saw the funny picture. "You all
need to go to the hairdresser!"

Talk about the story

Why did the family all have their hair cut?

Why did Jon want Kipper to keep still?

How did Kipper feel after his haircut?

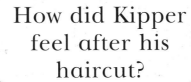

Why do you have your hair cut?

What do you find at the hairdresser?

Talk about the things you see on this page. Can you think of anything else you might find at the hairdresser?

Now look back at the story and find these things in the pictures.

back mirror

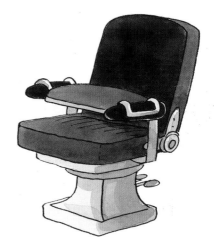

chair with special seat

combs

water spray

scissors

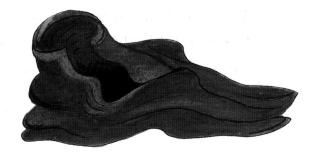

gown

brushes

hairdryer

wall mirror

magazines

Spot the difference

Find the five differences in the two pictures of Kipper.

First Experiences

More books for you to enjoy

Level 1: Getting Ready

Level 2: Starting to Read

Level 3: Becoming a Reader

Level 4: Building Confidence

Level 5: Reading with Confidence

OXFORD
UNIVERSITY PRESS

Great Clarendon Street,
Oxford OX2 6DP

Text © Roderick Hunt and
Annemarie Young 2007
Illustrations © Alex Brychta 2007

This edition published 2009

Read at Home Series Editors: Kate Ruttle, Annemarie Young

British Library Cataloguing in Publication Data available

ISBN: 9780198475262

10 9 8 7 6 5 4 3 2 1

Printed in China by Imago